The Pesky Parrot

Written by Lisa Thompson
Pictures by Craig Smith

"We need a new ship,"
said the Captain.
"Let's take that one."

The pirates fired the cannons.

"Take that!" they shouted.

3

"Look out! Here we come!"
shouted the pirates.

"Get off. Get off, Pesky Pirates,"
said the parrot.

"Hands up!" shouted the pirates.

The pirates took over the ship.

"Put up the pirate flag!"
shouted the Captain.

"Pesky Pirates," said the parrot.

The pirates tied up the crew
of the ship.

They tied up the parrot, too.

"A parrot is a good pet for a pirate,"
said the Cook. "Let's keep it!"

"Walk the plank!" shouted the Captain.
"This is our ship now."

The Captain did not make the parrot
walk the plank.

"This is my parrot now,"
he said.

The Captain put the parrot in a cage.

"Pretty parrot," said the Captain.
"Pretty parrot."

The parrot said nothing.

So the Captain let the parrot
out of the cage.

"Say something," said the Captain.

The parrot bit him on the finger.

"Pesky Pirate," she said.
"Pesky Pirate."

"You're a pesky parrot,"
said the Captain,
"and I'm going to
call you Fingers!"